Garfield

To Eat O...?
(That is a silly question.)

JIM DAVIS

RR

© 1998 PAWS INCORPORATED
(www.garfield.com)

All rights reserved

First published by Ravette Publishing1998

Printed and bound in Great Britain
for Ravette Publishing Limited,
Unit 3, Tristar Centre,
Star Road, Partridge Green,
West Sussex RH13 8RA
by Cox & Wyman Ltd, Reading, Berkshire

ISBN 1 85304 991 3

© 1996 PAWS, INC./Distributed by Universal Press Syndicate

HOW COME I JUST SAW A MOUSE RUNNING ACROSS THIS TABLE?!

NORMALLY YOU WOULDN'T

BUT FAT EDDIE'S PRETTY SLOW

© 1996 PAWS, INC./Distributed by Universal Press Syndicate

JiM DAViS 3-14

© 1996 PAWS, INC./Distributed by Universal Press Syndicate

© 1996 PAWS, INC./Distributed by Universal Press Syndicate

Dear Sir:
On behalf of spider lovers everywhere, we wish to strongly protest your brutal treatment of our arachnid brothers and sisters.

Spiders are our friends.
Spiders...

SMACK

JIM DAVIS 4-6

© 1996 PAWS, INC./Distributed by Universal Press Syndicate

© 1996 PAWS, INC./Distributed by Universal Press Syndicate

© 1996 PAWS, INC./Distributed by Universal Press Syndicate

JPM DAVIS 5-1

JIM DAVIS 5-9

© 1996 PAWS, INC./Distributed by Universal Press Syndicate

JIM DAVIS 6-11

© 1996 PAWS, INC./Distributed by Universal Press Syndicate

PAT
PAT
PAT

THERE!

JIM DAVIS 2-6

TAP
TAP

JIM DAVIS 2-8

© 1996 PAWS, INC./Distributed by Universal Press Syndicate

© 1996 PAWS, INC./Distributed by Universal Press Syndicate

OTHER GARFIELD BOOKS AVAILABLE

Classics @ £4.99 each　　　　　　　ISBN
Volume One　　　　　　　　　　　　1 85304 970 0
Volume Two　　　　　　　　　　　　1 85304 971 9

Miscellaneous
Garfield Treasury　　£9.99　　　　　1 85304 975 1

Garfield Address & Birthday　　　　　1 85304 918 2
Book Gift Set　　　£7.99 inc VAT

All Garfield books are available at your local bookshop or from the address below. Just tick the titles required and send the form with your remittance to:-

　B.B.C.S., P.O. BOX 941, HULL, NORTH HUMBERSIDE HU1 3YQ
　　24 Hour Telephone Credit Card Line 01482 224626
　Prices and availability are subject to change without notice.

Please enclose a cheque or postal order made payable to B.B.C.S. to the value of the cover price of the book and allow the following for postage and packing:

U.K. & B.F.P.O:　　£1.00 for the first book and 50p for each additional book to a maximum of £3.50.

Overseas &　　　　£2.00 for the first book, £1.00 for the second
Eire　　　　　　　and 50p for each additional book.

BLOCK CAPITALS PLEASE

Name ....

Address...

....

....

Cards accepted: Mastercard and Visa

Expiry Date ....Signature ....